go! CHINESE

聽説讀打寫

GO 100

Workbook
(Traditional Character Edition)

羅秋昭
Julie LO

薛意梅
Emily YIH

CENGAGE
Learning·

Andover • Melbourne • Mexico City • Stamford, CT • Toronto • Hong Kong • New Delhi • Seoul • Singapore • Tokyo

Go! Chinese Go100 Workbook
(Traditional Character Edition)

Julie Lo, Emily Yih

Senior Director, Publishing/CLT:
Roy Lee

Editorial Manager, CLT:
Lan Zhao

Development Editor:
Coco Koh

Senior Product Manager (Asia):
Joyce Tan

Product Manager (Outside Asia):
Mei Yun Loh

Production Manager:
Pauline Lim

Production Executive:
Evan Wu

Editor, ELT:
Yuan Ting Soh

For product information and technology assistance, contact us at
Cengage Learning Asia Customer Support, 65-6410-1200

For permission to use material from this text or product,
submit all requests online at **www.cengageasia.com/permissions**
Further permission questions can be emailed to
asia.permissionrequest@cengage.com

ISBN-13: 978-981-4226-92-9
ISBN-10: 981-4226-92-0

Cengage Learning Asia Pte Ltd
151 Lorong Chuan
#02-08 New Tech Park
Singapore 556741

Cengage Learning is a leading provider of customized learning solutions with office locations around the globe, including Andover, Melbourne, Mexico City, Stamford (CT), Toronto, Hong Kong, New Delhi, Seoul, Singapore, and Tokyo. Locate your local office at **www.cengage.com/global**

Cengage Learning products are represented in Canada by Nelson Education, Ltd.

For product information, visit **www.cengageasia.com**

Photo credits:
Cover: © Charly Franklin/Taxi/Getty Images.

Printed in Taiwan
12 13 14 15 16 15 14 13

Preface

Go! Chinese, together with *IQChinese Go* **multimedia CD-ROM**, is a fully integrated Chinese language program that offers an easy, enjoyable, and effective learning experience for learners of Chinese as a foreign language.

The Workbook is an essential component of the *Go! Chinese* series. The exercises are closely linked to the content of each lesson, allowing students to solidify their understanding of and review the lesson learned in the classroom.

The Workbook features the following types of exercises:

- **Foundation Building Exercises**

  Phonetics (*pinyin*), Chinese radicals, vocabulary review, sentence re-ordering, and translation are examples of foundation building exercises. These exercises help students systematically build a solid foundation in the Chinese language.

- **Problem-Solving Exercises**

  Exercises such as crossword puzzles, composing short conversations, and answering questions involving the interpretation of graphs or pictures, provide students with interesting and challenging opportunities to learn the Chinese language through problem-solving tasks.

- **Chinese Typing Exercises**

  The unique characteristic of this series is the use of Chinese typing as an instructional strategy to improve word recognition, listening, and pronunciation skills. The typing activity can be found in the CD-ROM. Students are asked to type characters or sentences as they are read aloud or displayed on the computer screen. They will be alerted if they make a mistake and will be given the chance to correct them. If they do not get it right on the third try, the software provides immediate feedback on how to correct the error. This interactive trial-and-error process allows students to develop self-confidence and learn by doing. Students can use the chart in the Workbook to record their best timing for these typing activities (Sentence Quiz). Students can also separately keep a list of words that they frequently have trouble with for future review.

  The Sentence Quiz exercise comprises four levels.

  ➤ Level 1 – Warm-up Quiz (Look, Listen, and Type): Chinese text, *pinyin*, and audio prompts are provided.

  ➤ Level 2 – Visual-aid Quiz: Only Chinese text is provided. There are no *pinyin* or audio prompts.

  ➤ Level 3 – Audio-aid Quiz: Only audio prompts are provided.

  ➤ Level 4 – Character-selection Quiz : Only Chinese text is provided. After entering the correct *pinyin*, students are required to select the correct character from a list of similar looking characters.

- **Word Recognition and Character Writing Exercises**

  To help students learn to read and recognize actual Chinese characters, *pinyin* is generally not annotated in the Workbook, except for certain *pinyin*, writing, and vocabulary exercises.

  The Workbook also provides Chinese character writing worksheets for a subset of the vocabulary to help students understand and appreciate the characteristics and formation of Chinese characters. Writing can help student remember the Chinese characters better. The writing sheets illustrate the correct stroke order of each character. Grid lines and traceable characters are also provided to help students trace and copy characters until they are able to write them independently. The teacher may assign additional character writing practice according to learning emphasis and needs.

- **Review Units**

  Two Review units are provided after every five lessons in the Workbook. They give students the opportunity to review and reflect on their knowledge and progress, and reinforce what they have learned. Teachers may have students work on these units individually as homework, or go over them together in class.

The Workbook is designed to enable students to complete all exercises independently, either in class, or at home. Students should not have to spend more than 15 minutes on each page. Between one and two pages can be assigned as individual assignment after every two classroom sessions. Teachers may also wish to encourage students to spend 10 minutes a day on the Sentence Quiz exercise in the CD-ROM.

Table of Contents

One Two Three

1 Complete the table below. Write the missing Chinese number, *pinyin*, or cross out the circles.

	Chinese	*pinyin*	Cross out the circles
1	二	èr	⊗ ⊗ ○ ○ ○ / ○ ○ ○ ○ ○
2	五		○ ○ ○ ○ ○ / ○ ○ ○ ○ ○
3	九		○ ○ ○ ○ ○ / ○ ○ ○ ○ ○
4			⊗ ⊗ ⊗ ⊗ ⊗ / ⊗ ⊗ ○ ○ ○
5			⊗ ○ ○ ○ ○ / ○ ○ ○ ○ ○
6	三		○ ○ ○ ○ ○ / ○ ○ ○ ○ ○
7	十		○ ○ ○ ○ ○ / ○ ○ ○ ○ ○
8			⊗ ⊗ ⊗ ⊗ ○ / ○ ○ ○ ○ ○
9	八		○ ○ ○ ○ ○ / ○ ○ ○ ○ ○
10			⊗ ⊗ ⊗ ⊗ ⊗ / ⊗ ○ ○ ○ ○

② Practice the strokes and write the characters.

yī	èr	sān	sì	wǔ
一	二	三	四	五

liù	qī	bā	jiǔ	shí
六	七	八	九	十

一

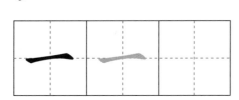

二 二

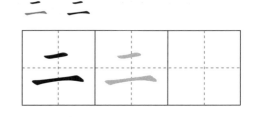

三 三 三

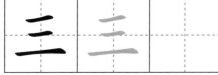

四 四 四 四 四

五 五 五 五

六 六 六 六

七 七

八 八

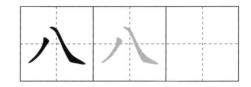

九 九

十 十

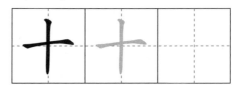

3 Write the numbers in Chinese.

1 43: 四十三

2 78: _____

3 12: _____

4 200: _____

5 55: _____

6 37: _____

7 69: _____

8 900: _____

9 96: _____

10 20: _____

Typing Records Go 100

4 Go to the *Exercise > Sentence Quiz* in your Go100 CD and take the quiz (Level 1 or 2). Choose the best two results.

Record	Date	Time Elapsed	Sentence Quiz (Level 1 or 2)	Accurate Spelling per Minute
1				
2				

5 Put a tick (✓) beside the correct answer.

①

nán shēng
- [✓] 兩個男生
- [ ] 二個男生

②

-19-20- **?** -22-23-

- [ ] 兩十一
- [ ] 二十一

③

▲▲▲▲▲▲
▲▲▲▲▲▲

- [ ] 十兩個
- [ ] 十二個

④

232

- [ ] 兩百三十兩
- [ ] 二百三十二

⑤ I have two good friends.

wǒ yǒu   hǎo péng yǒu
- [ ] 我有兩個好朋友。
- [ ] 我有兩好朋友。

6 Write the correct number in the space provided such that the sum of each pair of opposite numbers is 50.

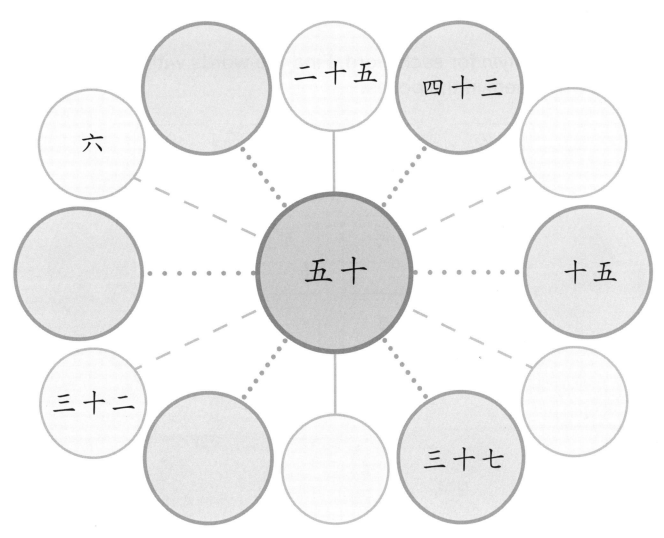

7 Go to the *Exercise > Sentence Quiz* in your Go100 CD and take the quiz (Level 3 or 4). Choose the best two results.

Record	Date	Time Elapsed	Sentence Quiz (Level 3 or 4)	Accurate Spelling per Minute
1				
2				

2

你好嗎？
How Are You?

1 Write the *pinyin* for each word. Find the words with the Final "a" and write them in the boxes.

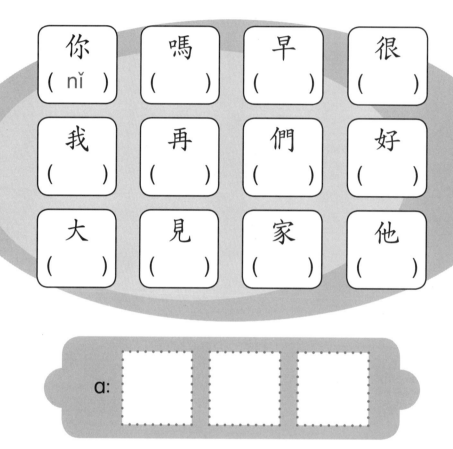

你 (nǐ)　嗎 ( )　早 ( )　很 ( )

我 ( )　再 ( )　們 ( )　好 ( )

大 ( )　見 ( )　家 ( )　他 ( )

a: ☐ ☐ ☐

2 Read the words below. Identify the phrases with two third tones and write them on the blanks.

很好、五個、再見、十九、好嗎
你早、兩百、十四、你好、大家

＿＿＿＿、＿＿＿＿、＿＿＿＿、

3 Write the meaning of each phrase on the space provided.

1 大家： everybody

2 我： _____

3 我們： _____

4 你： _____

5 你們： _____

6 你好： _____

7 他們： _____

8 你好嗎？： _____

9 大家早： _____

10 我很好： _____

4 Go to the *Exercise > Sentence Quiz* in your Go100 CD and take the quiz (Level 1 or 2). Choose the best two results.

Record	Date	Time Elapsed	Sentence Quiz (Level 1 or 2)	Accurate Spelling per Minute
1				
2				

5 Practice the strokes and write the characters.

wǒ　nǐ　tā　dà　hǎo
我　你　他　大　好

☺：__大__家好！你____嗎？　●：____很好。
　　　dà　　　　　hǎo　　　　　wǒ

　　　　　●：_____ _____嗎？　☺：____很好。
　　　　　　　　tā　　　hǎo　　　　　　tā

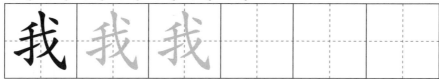

我 我 我 我 我 我 我

你 你 你 你 你 你 你

他 他 他 他 他

大 大 大

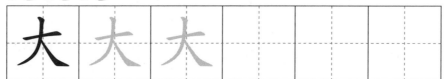

好 好 好 好 好 好

你好嗎？

6 Read the dialogues. Put a tick (✓) in the box if they are correct, and a cross (✗) if they are wrong.

7 The Initials, Finals, and tone mark on the right can be used to form the *pinyin* of one of the phrases on the left. Put a tick (✓) beside the correct answer.

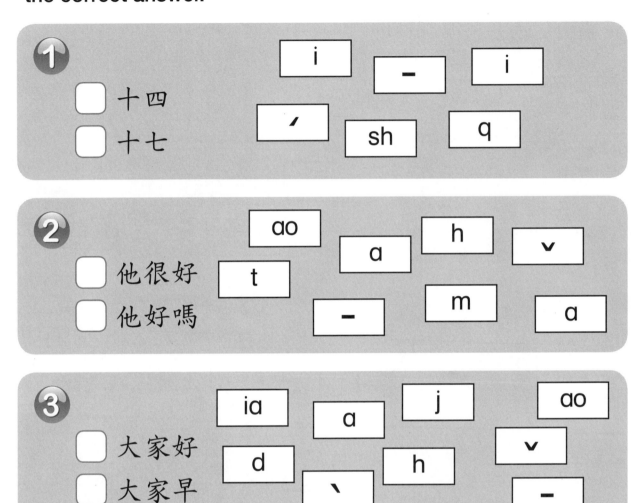

①
- 十四
- 十七

i　　—　　i
´　　sh　　q

②
- 他很好
- 他好嗎

ao　　h　　ˇ
a
t　　—　　m　　a

③
- 大家好
- 大家早

ia　　j　　ao
a　　　　ˇ
d　　h
ヽ　　　—

Typing Records 〔Go 100〕

8 Go to the *Exercise > Sentence Quiz* in your Go100 CD and take the quiz (Level 3 or 4). Choose the best two results.

Record	Date	Time Elapsed	Sentence Quiz (Level 3 or 4)	Accurate Spelling per Minute
1				
2				

謝謝你！
Thank You!

1 Complete the speech bubbles with the phrases below to create conversations.

① 不客氣。 ② 對不起！ ③ 謝謝你！

④ 你好嗎？ ⑤ 沒關係！ ⑥ 我很好，謝謝！

2 Mark the tone of the words in the phrases.

①	對不起	duì bù qǐ
②	沒關係	mei guan xi
③	謝謝你	xie xie ni
④	不客氣	bu ke qi
⑤	不用謝	bu yong xie
⑥	再見	zai jian
⑦	大家早	da jia zao
⑧	他很好	ta hen hao

Typing Records Go 100

3 Go to the *Exercise > Sentence Quiz* in your Go100 CD and take the quiz (Level 1 or 2). Choose the best two results.

Record	Date	Time Elapsed	Sentence Quiz *(Level 1 or 2)*	Accurate Spelling per Minute
1				
2				

4 Practice the strokes to write the characters.

qǐng	bù	yòng	duì	méi
請	不	用	對	沒

☺：謝謝你！ ☻：____ ____ ____客氣。
　　　　　　　　　　qǐng　bú　yòng

☺：____ ____起！ ☻：____關係。
　　　duì　bù　　　　méi

請 請 請 請 請 請 請 請 請 請 請 請 請 請 請

請	請	請				

不 不 不 不

不	不	不				

用 用 用 用 用

用	用	用				

對 對 對 對 對 對 對 對 對 對 對 對 對 對

對	對	對				

沒 沒 沒 沒 沒 沒 沒

沒	沒	沒				

5 Circle the words that have the Finals "uan", "iu", and "ie".

① uan
三　家
見　關

② iu
九　對
六　用

③ ie
沒　們
謝　個

6 Write the meaning of the phrases below in English.

① 對不起：_____

② 謝謝你：_____

③ 沒關係：_____

④ 不客氣：_____

⑤ 不用謝：_____

7 Change the following from the positive form to the negative form.

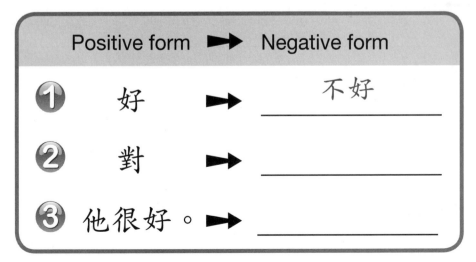

Positive form	➡	Negative form
① 好	➡	不好
② 對	➡	_____
③ 他很好。	➡	_____

8 Find the radical components of the characters, and write their corresponding numbers in the boxes.

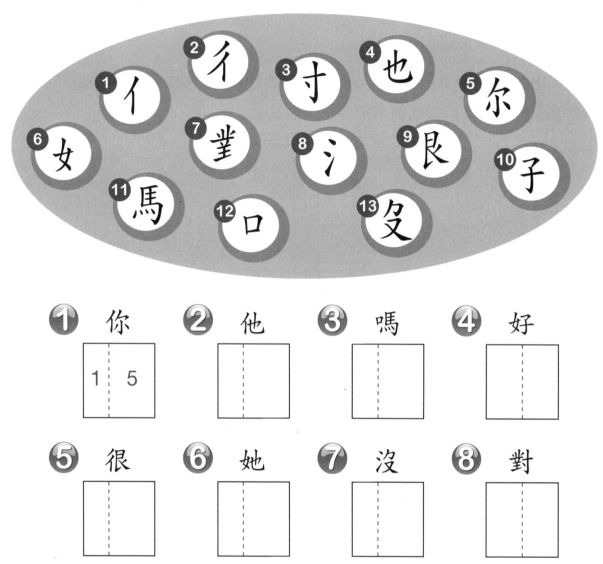

① 你

1	5

② 他

③ 嗎

④ 好

⑤ 很

⑥ 她

⑦ 沒

⑧ 對

Typing Records Go 100

9 Go to the *Exercise > Sentence Quiz* in your Go100 CD and take the quiz (Level 3 or 4). Choose the best two results.

Record	Date	Time Elapsed	Sentence Quiz (Level 3 or 4)	Accurate Spelling per Minute
1				
2				

姓什麼？

What Is Your Last Name?

1 Write the *pinyin* for each word. Find the words with Final "ing" and "en" and write them in the boxes.

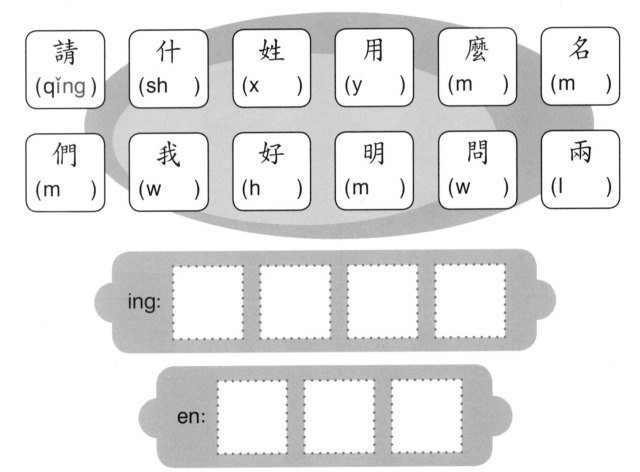

請
(qǐng)

什
(sh)

姓
(x)

用
(y)

麼
(m)

名
(m)

們
(m)

我
(w)

好
(h)

明
(m)

問
(w)

兩
(l)

ing:

en:

2 Match the characters that can form phrases and write out the meaning of each phrase.

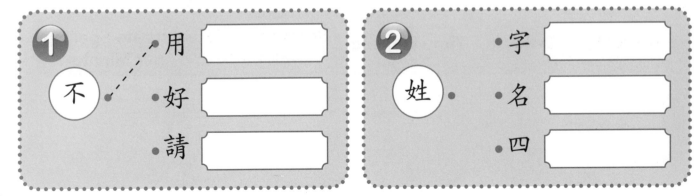

① 不

• 用

• 好

• 請

② 姓

• 字

• 名

• 四

3 Find and circle the Chinese phrases that match the meaning of the English words on the right.

請①	什	麼
問	再	不
大	家	客
貴	姓	氣
見	名	字

① may I ask

② you're welcome

③ first name

④ everybody

⑤ last name (formal)

4 Complete each sentence using the words in the brackets.

① 我 ＿＿＿（姓 / 叫）謝小明。

② ＿＿＿（請 / 我）問你叫什麼名字？

③ 你姓謝，他姓謝，我姓謝，大家＿＿＿（都 / 不）姓謝。

Typing Records Go100

5 Go to the *Exercise > Sentence Quiz* in your Go100 CD and take the quiz (Level 1 or 2). Choose the best two results.

Record	Date	Time Elapsed	Sentence Quiz (Level 1 or 2)	Accurate Spelling per Minute
1				
2				

Practice the strokes and write the characters.

wèn	jiào	míng	zì	de
問	叫	名	字	的

☺：請＿＿你＿＿什麼＿＿ ＿＿？
        wèn   jiào   míng zi

●：我＿＿ ＿＿ ＿＿ ＿＿王大關。
    de   míng   zi   jiào

問 問 問 問 問 問 問 問 問 問 問

問	問	問			

叫 叫 叫 叫 叫

叫	叫	叫			

名 名 名 名 名 名

名	名	名			

字 字 字 字 字 字

字	字	字			

的 的 的 的 的 的 的 的

的	的	的			

7 Read the words in the speech bubbles. Answer the questions by putting a tick (✓) beside the correct answer.

> He is my brother. His first name is the same as my friend's, 謝小貴.

王大關

1 What is his brother's full name?

☐ 王小關   ☐ 王小貴

☐ 謝大關   ☐ 關小貴

> She is my friend. We have the same first name, but our last name is different. My friend's last name is the same as my cousin's, 謝好.

王家家

2 What is her friend's full name?

☐ 好家家   ☐ 謝好

☐ 謝家家   ☐ 家謝

8 The radical of the characters below are missing. Write the correct radical "亻"or "女" in the space provided.

① 我 ⬚生 王，叫大關。

② ◕：請問 ⬚尔 叫什麼名字？ ◔：我叫John。

③ 我 ⬚門 都姓謝。

④ ⬚也 的名字叫David。

⑤ ◕：Michelle好嗎？ ◔： ⬚也 很好。

⑥ 請問小明姓 ⬚十 麼？

Typing Records [Go100]

9 Go to the *Exercise > Sentence Quiz* in your Go100 CD and take the quiz (Level 3 or 4). Choose the best two results.

Record	Date	Time Elapsed	Sentence Quiz (Level 3 or 4)	Accurate Spelling per Minute
1				
2				

星期幾？

What Day Is
Today?

1 Look at the calendar and fill in the blanks with the correct answer.

十二月

Today

Sun.	Mon.	Tue.	Wed.	Thu.	Fri.	Sat.
		1	2	3	4	5
6	7	8	9	10	11	12
13	14	15	16	17	18	19
20	21	22	23	24	25	26
27	28	29	30	31		

❶ 今天是 ＿＿＿＿月＿＿＿＿日星期＿＿＿＿，

昨天是 ＿＿＿＿月＿＿＿＿日星期＿＿＿＿，

明天是 ＿＿＿＿月＿＿＿＿日星期＿＿＿＿。

❷ 十二月十日是星期＿＿＿＿。

❸ 十二月有＿＿＿＿個星期二。

2 Fill in the missing Initials to form the *pinyin*.

❶ 期（ qí ）　❷ 日（　ì ）　❸ 幾（　ǐ ）

❹ 天（　iān）　❺ 年（　ián）　❻ 見（　iàn）

3 Study the calendars and the hints to find the answer.

January						
Su	M	Tu	W	Th	F	Sa
				1	2	3
4	5	6	7	8	9	10
11	12	13	14	15	16	17
18	19	20	21	22	23	24
25	26	27	28	29	30	31

February						
Su	M	Tu	W	Th	F	Sa
1	2	3	4	5	6	7
8	9	10	11	12	13	14
15	16	17	18	19	20	21
22	23	24	25	26	27	28

March						
Su	M	Tu	W	Th	F	Sa
1	2	3	4	5	6	7
8	9	10	11	12	13	14
15	16	17	18	19	20	21
22	23	24	25	26	27	28
29	30	31				

April						
Su	M	Tu	W	Th	F	Sa
			1	2	3	4
5	6	7	8	9	10	11
12	13	14	15	16	17	18
19	20	21	22	23	24	25
26	27	28	29	30		

May						
Su	M	Tu	W	Th	F	Sa
					1	2
3	4	5	6	7	8	9
10	11	12	13	14	15	16
17	18	19	20	21	22	23
24	25	26	27	28	29	30
31						

June						
Su	M	Tu	W	Th	F	Sa
	1	2	3	4	5	6
7	8	9	10	11	12	13
14	15	16	17	18	19	20
21	22	23	24	25	26	27
28	29	30				

July						
Su	M	Tu	W	Th	F	Sa
			1	2	3	4
5	6	7	8	9	10	11
12	13	14	15	16	17	18
19	20	21	22	23	24	25
26	27	28	29	30	31	

August						
Su	M	Tu	W	Th	F	Sa
						1
2	3	4	5	6	7	8
9	10	11	12	13	14	15
16	17	18	19	20	21	22
23	24	25	26	27	28	29
30	31					

September						
Su	M	Tu	W	Th	F	Sa
		1	2	3	4	5
6	7	8	9	10	11	12
13	14	15	16	17	18	19
20	21	22	23	24	25	26
27	28	29	30			

October						
Su	M	Tu	W	Th	F	Sa
				1	2	3
4	5	6	7	8	9	10
11	12	13	14	15	16	17
18	19	20	21	22	23	24
25	26	27	28	29	30	31

November						
Su	M	Tu	W	Th	F	Sa
1	2	3	4	5	6	7
8	9	10	11	12	13	14
15	16	17	18	19	20	21
22	23	24	25	26	27	28
29	30					

December						
Su	M	Tu	W	Th	F	Sa
		1	2	3	4	5
6	7	8	9	10	11	12
13	14	15	16	17	18	19
20	21	22	23	24	25	26
27	28	29	30	31		

❶ 這個月有三十一天。

❷ 這個月有五個星期日。

❸ 這個月有四個星期二。

❹ 這個月的十九日不是星期三。

這個月是＿＿＿＿月。

Typing Records **Go 100**

4 Go to the *Exercise > Sentence Quiz* in your Go100 CD and take the quiz (Level 1 or 2). Choose the best two results.

Record	Date	Time Elapsed	Sentence Quiz (Level 1 or 2)	Accurate Spelling per Minute
1				
2				

5 Fill in the blanks with the correct answer.

1 一個星期有_____天，一年有_____個月。

2 Monday是星期_____；Wednesday是星期_____。

3 今天是星期六，昨天是_____，明天是

_____。

4 _____是二〇〇八年，_____是二〇〇九年，

明年是二〇一〇年。

5 九月 _____（沒有 / 有）三十一日。

6 March 16：_____月_____日

7 November 7, 2009：_____

⑥ Practice the strokes to write the characters.

yǒu	yuè	tiān	jīn	rì
有	月	天	今	日

一年＿＿＿十二個＿＿＿，一個星期＿＿＿＿七＿＿＿＿。
        yǒu   yuè   yǒu   tiān

＿＿＿＿＿ ＿＿＿＿＿是星期六，明＿＿＿＿是星期＿＿＿＿。
  jīn   tiān   tiān   rì

有 有 有 有 有 有

有	有	有			

月 月 月 月

月	月	月			

天 天 天 天

天	天	天			

今 今 今 今

今	今	今			

日 日 日 日

日	日	日			

7 Group the words according to the positions (left and right, top and bottom) of their radicals.

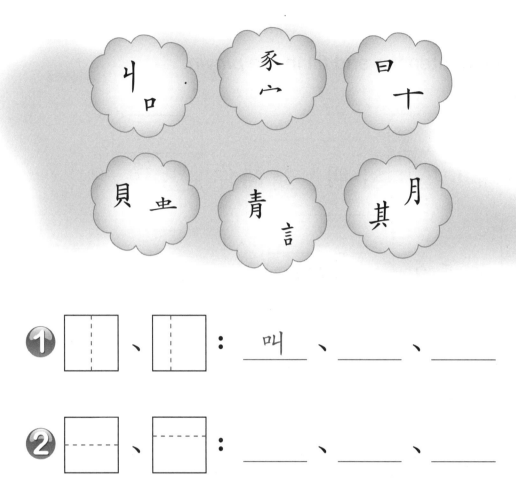

① ⬚ 、 ⬚ : 叫 、 ＿＿＿ 、 ＿＿＿

② ⬚ 、 ⬚ : ＿＿＿ 、 ＿＿＿ 、 ＿＿＿

8 Go to the *Exercise > Sentence Quiz* in your Go100 CD and take the quiz (Level 3 or 4). Choose the best two results.

Record	Date	Time Elapsed	Sentence Quiz (Level 3 or 4)	Accurate Spelling per Minute
1				
2				

REVIEW 1

1 Read the sentences and fill in the *pinyin*.

① 我姓謝，□ 叫 小明。請問你 □ 貴姓 ？

② □ 你 好嗎？ □ 我很好 。

③ □ 謝謝 你！ □ 不客氣 。

④ Ada 好嗎？ 她 □ 不好 ，她生病了 _{shēng bìng} (sick)。

⑤ 今天是 □ 五 月 □ 七 日 □ 星期一 。

⑥ □ 這是 我的書 _{shū} (book)。

⑦ 我們 □ 都 叫小明，我們都不 □ 姓 □ 謝 。

2 Read the paragraphs and put a tick (✓) beside the correct answer.

大家好，我叫關大中。我有七個好朋友，四個是
男生，三個是女生。
<small>nán shēng</small>　<small>nǚ shēng</small>

① 關大中姓什麼？

☐ 關　☐ 大關　☐ 中　☐ 大中

② 他有幾個好朋友？

☐ 十四個　☐ 四個　☐ 七個　☐ 三個

今年是二〇〇九年，二月沒有二十九日。今天是
二月二十八日星期六。

① 這個月有幾天？

☐ 三十一天　☐ 二十九天
☐ 三十天　☐ 二十八天

② 明天是幾月幾日星期幾？

☐ 明天是二月二十九日星期七。
☐ 明天是二月二十九日星期日。
☐ 明天是三月一日星期一。
☐ 明天是三月一日星期天。

3 Answer the questions using the words in the box.

去年	今年	今天	明天	這個月
什麼	姓	叫	名字	貴姓

1 ＿＿＿＿＿＿＿是四月三日，請問明天是幾月幾日？

2 我叫謝小明，請問你＿＿＿＿＿＿＿？

3 😀：請問＿＿＿＿＿＿＿是幾月？　　😀：十二月。

4 😀：請問你叫什麼名字？

　　😀：我＿＿＿＿＿＿＿王，＿＿＿＿＿＿＿大關。

4 Using the words in the box, write four lines of dialogue for the picture below.

A 對不起。	**B** 再見。	**C** 我不好。
D 不客氣。	**E** 你好。	**F** 你叫什麼名字？
G 沒關係。	**H** 謝謝！	**I** 我叫＿＿＿＿＿＿。
J 你好嗎？	**K** 我很好。	

_____

_____

_____

_____

5 Answer the following questions.

Tomorrow

十月

Sun.	Mon.	Tue.	Wed.	Thu.	Fri.	Sat.
				1	2	3
4	5	6	7	8	9	10
11	12	13	14	15	16	17
18	19	20	21	22	23	24
25	26	27	28	29	30	

1 今天是_____月_____日星期_____，
昨天是_____月_____日星期_____。

2 十月三十日是星期_____。

3 十月十三日是星期_____。

4 十月_____（有／沒有）三十一天，
十月是_____（大／小）月。

5 十月有_____個星期天。

6 十月三日到十月十九日有_____天。

7 十月的下一個月 (the next month) 是幾月？_____月。

6 The calendar has been smeared with some ink. Using the hints below, deduce today's date.

2009
June
1

六月						
Su	M	Tu	W	Th	F	Sa
	1	2	3	4	5	6
7	8	9	10	11	12	13
14	15	16	17	18	19	20
21	22	23	24	25	26	27
28	29	30				

七月						
Su	M	Tu	W	Th	F	Sa
			1	2	3	4
5	6	7	8	9	10	11
12	13	14	15	16	17	18
19	20	21	22	23	24	25
26	27	28	29	30	31	

八月						
Su	M	Tu	W	Th	F	Sa
						1
2	3	4	5	6	7	8
9	10	11	12	13	14	15
16	17	18	19	20	21	22
23	24	25	26	27	28	29
30	31					

❶ 昨天不是星期三，不是星期五。

❷ 明天不是星期二，不是星期四。

❸ 今天不是星期二，不是星期五。

① 請問今天是星期幾？

_____

② 請問今天是幾月幾日？

_____

7

Using the prompts below, write the corresponding Chinese character in the boxes.

		(3)			
(A) 大	家	好		(5)	
				(B)	
(C)(1)		(D)		(E)	
		(4)		,	
	(F)(2)				
(G)					

Vertical	Horizontal
1 not at all	**A** Hello, everybody!
2 this year	**B** full name
3 How are you?	**C** haven't
4 Sunday	**D** Don't mention it.
5 My last name is Xie and my first name is Xiao Ming.	**E** Thanks!
	F today
	G the next year

幾個人？

How Many People Are
There in Your Family?

1 Read the Chinese characters. Then write the *pinyin* and the
meaning of the words in the spaces provided.

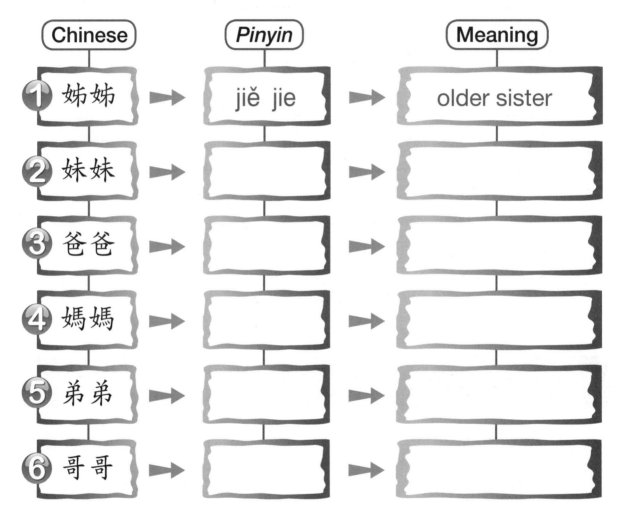

Chinese	Pinyin	Meaning
① 姊姊	jiě jie	older sister
② 妹妹		
③ 爸爸		
④ 媽媽		
⑤ 弟弟		
⑥ 哥哥		

2 Find the words with Finals "a" or "ou" in Lesson 6, and write the
pinyin for each word in the blanks.

a: ____bà____ 、 _____

ou : _____

❸ Read the questions and put a tick (✓) beside the correct answer.

① 你家有幾口人？
- [ ] 我有哥哥，沒有妹妹。
- [✓] 我家一共有七口人。

② 你有幾個哥哥？
- [ ] 我有一個弟弟。
- [ ] 我有一個哥哥。

③ 你有弟弟嗎？
- [ ] 你有兩個弟弟。
- [ ] 我有兩個弟弟。

④ 你妹妹叫什麼名字？
- [ ] 她叫Alice。
- [ ] 她妹妹叫Alice。

⑤ 你有沒有姊姊？
- [ ] 我有一個姊姊。
- [ ] 我沒有一個姊姊。

⑥ 你有哥哥嗎？
- [ ] 我還有一個哥哥。
- [ ] 我沒有哥哥。

Typing Records ⟨Go 100⟩

❹ Go to the *Exercise > Sentence Quiz* in your Go100 CD and take the quiz (Level 1 or 2). Choose the best two results.

Record	Date	Time Elapsed	Sentence Quiz (Level 1 or 2)	Accurate Spelling per Minute
1				
2				

5 Practice the strokes and write the characters.

kǒu	rén	bà	mā	hái
口	人	爸	媽	還

我家有三＿＿＿ ＿＿＿，＿＿＿ ＿＿＿、

kǒu　　rén　　　bà　　ba

＿＿＿ ＿＿＿，＿＿＿有我。

mā　　ma　　　hái

口 口 口

口	口	口			

人 人

人	人	人			

爸 爸 爸 爸 爸 爸 爸 爸

爸	爸	爸			

媽 媽 媽 媽 媽 媽 媽 媽 媽 媽 媽 媽 媽

媽	媽	媽			

還 還 還 還 還 還 還 還 還 還 還 還 還

還 還 還 還

還	還	還			

Imagine you are the character in the picture. Using the helping words in the brackets, write three sentences to introduce your family members.

①

- 我家一共五口人。 _____ （一共）
- _____ （沒有）
- _____ （有……，還有……）

②

- _____ （兩個）
- _____ （弟弟／妹妹）
- _____ （七口人）

7 Answer the following questions.

1 You are at your friend's house and see a boy younger than you. You would like to know who he is. You may ask:

請問他是你（ 　　　　　　　　 ）嗎？

2 You would like to know if your friend has an older brother. You may ask:

_____

3 If you are the youngest in your family and someone asks you, "你沒有妹妹嗎？", you may answer (start your reply with either "對" or "不對"):

_____

4 If someone asks you how many people there are in your family and who they are, you may reply:

_____

Typing Records Go 100

8 Go to the *Exercise > Sentence Quiz* in your Go100 CD and take the quiz (Level 3 or 4). Choose the best two results.

Record	Date	Time Elapsed	Sentence Quiz (Level 3 or 4)	Accurate Spelling per Minute
1				
2				

多少錢？
How Much Is This?

1 Use the information in the box and fill in the blanks with the appropriate Chinese words. Each boy must buy three different items. He can purchase two or more of each item.

 有75塊　　 有50塊　　 有92塊

1 買了一個 、五個 ，還有兩個 ，

一共＿＿＿＿塊錢，還有＿＿＿＿塊錢。

2 買了一個 、一個 、一個 ，還有

一個 ，一共＿＿＿＿塊錢，還有＿＿＿＿塊錢。

3 買了＿＿＿＿個 、＿＿＿＿個 ，還有

＿＿＿＿個 ，一共＿＿＿＿塊錢，還有三十塊錢。

2 Read the characters. Write the missing *pinyin* and mark the tone for each word.

① 太（tài　） ② 錢（q　） ③ 買（m　） ④ 算（s　）

⑤ 便（p　） ⑥ 塊（k　） ⑦ 點（d　） ⑧ 還（h　）

3 Complete each sentence using the words in the brackets.

① 這個太貴了，我＿＿＿＿＿（要／不）買。

② 今年二月＿＿＿＿＿（有／沒有）二十九日。

③ 請問你要買＿＿＿＿＿（這個／什麼）嗎？

④ 這個＿＿＿＿＿（很好／不好），我不要。

⑤ 我要買這個，請問這個＿＿＿＿＿（幾／多少）錢？

Typing Records > Go100

4 Go to the *Exercise > Sentence Quiz* in your Go100 CD and take the quiz (Level 1 or 2). Choose the best two results.

Record	Date	Time Elapsed	Sentence Quiz (Level 1 or 2)	Accurate Spelling per Minute
1				
2				

5 Practice the strokes and write the characters.

le	yào	mǎi	duō	shǎo
了	要	買	多	少

那個太貴____，我____ ____這個。
　　　　　　le　　　　yào　　mǎi

請問這個____ ____錢？
　　　　　duō　　shǎo

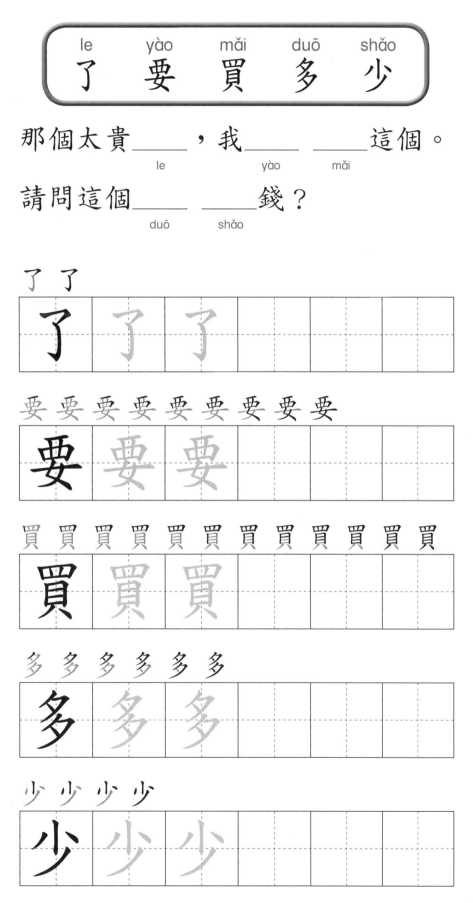

了 了

要 要 要 要 要 要 要 要 要

買 買 買 買 買 買 買 買 買 買 買 買

多 多 多 多 多 多

少 少 少 少

6 Circle the correct radical for each character. Then write the Chinese word in the bracket.

1. 女 + (生) 巳 丩 （ 姓 ）

2. 宀 + 一 子 口 （　）

3. 言 + 生 青 早 （　）

4. 亻 + 幾 月 尔 （　）

5. 西 + 人 女 口 （　）

6. 白 + 也 大 勹 （　）

7. 土 + 鬼 女 巴 （　）

8. 金 + 多 十 戔 （　）

多少錢？

7 Rearrange the words to form a complete sentence.

1 ❶買 ❷要 ❸你 ❹什麼
➡ (3 | 2 | 1 | 4) ？

2 ❶幾口 ❷有 ❸人 ❹你家 ❺請問
➡ (| | | |) ？

3 ❶這個 ❷請問 ❸錢 ❹多少
➡ (| | |) ？

4 ❶天 ❷多少 ❸有 ❹一年
➡ (| | |) ？

5 ❶不好 ❷便宜 ❸好 ❹一點兒
➡ (| | |) ？

Typing Records Go100

8 Go to the *Exercise > Sentence Quiz* in your Go100 CD and take the quiz (Level 3 or 4). Choose the best two results.

Record	Date	Time Elapsed	Sentence Quiz *(Level 3 or 4)*	Accurate Spelling per Minute
1				
2				

8

幾點鐘？
What Time Is It?

1 Draw the hands on the clock to show the correct time.

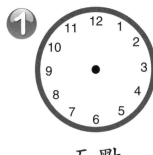
五點

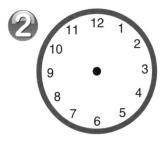
七點半

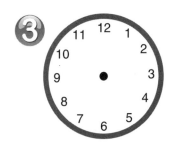
十二點十五分

2 Write the correct time in Chinese in the blanks provided.

_____ 點

_____ 分

_____ 點

_____ 分

_____ 點

_____ 分

_____ 點

_____ 分

_____ 點

_____ 分

_____ 點

_____ 分

42   幾點鐘？

③ Use "還有", "⋯⋯點鐘", or "⋯⋯點半" to describe the time.

① [08:23] ➡ 還有七分鐘八點半

② [09:54] ➡ _____

③ [10:15] ➡ _____

④ [11:47] ➡ _____

⑤ [05:20] ➡ _____

④ Complete the table using the flight information below.

	ARRIVING FROM	SCHEDULED ARRIVAL TIME	STATUS	ACTUAL ARRIVAL TIME
①	San Francisco	08:25	15-minute delay	(八點四十分)
②	Taipei	08:40	On time	( )
③	Singapore	09:50	13 minutes earlier	( )
④	Madrid	10:05	7 minutes earlier	( )
⑤	Toronto	10:35	25-minute delay	( )
⑥	Tokyo	11:02	On time	( )

5 Go to the *Exercise > Sentence Quiz* in your Go100 CD and take the quiz (Level 1 or 2). Choose the best two results.

Record	Date	Time Elapsed	Sentence Quiz (Level 1 or 2)	Accurate Spelling per Minute
1				
2				

6 The Initials, Finals, and tone mark on the right can be used to form the *pinyin* of one of the phrases on the left. Put a tick (✓) beside the correct answer and write its *pinyin* in the brackets.

1
- ☐ 晚上
- ☐ 上午

(_____)

w	sh	ˇ
an	ang	ˋ

2
- ☐ 便宜
- ☐ 一天

(_____)

ˋ	ian	t
–	yi	

3
- ☐ 七點半
- ☐ 幾點鐘

(_____)

–	ˇ	ˇ	zh
ong	d	ian	j
		i	

44 幾點鐘？

7 Practice the strokes and write the characters.

shàng	zhōng	xià	zài	zǒu
上	中	下	在	走

現____ ____午十二點，____午三點我要____。
　　zài　zhōng　　　　　xià　　　　　zǒu

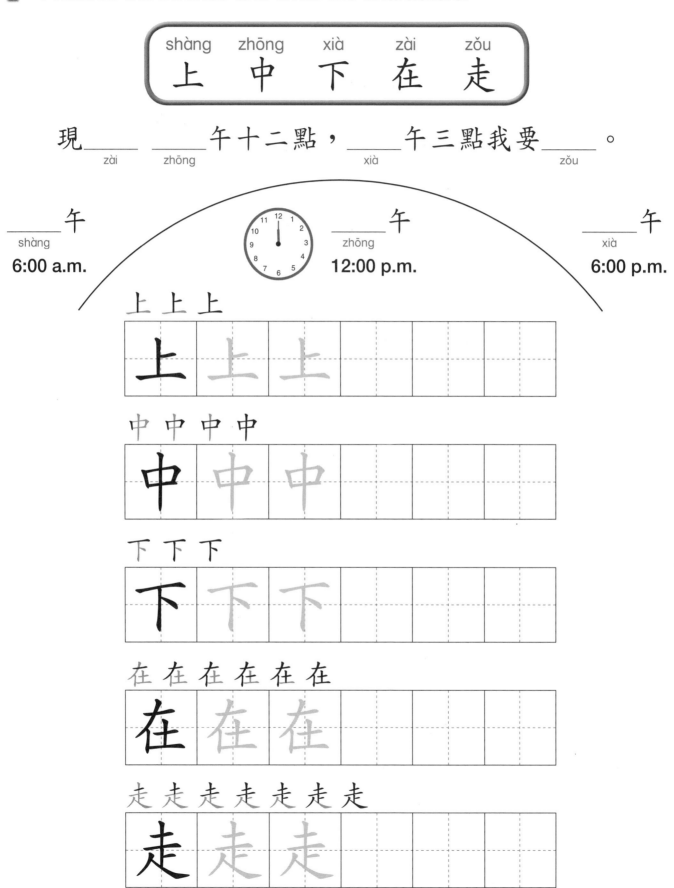

____午
shàng
6:00 a.m.

12:00 p.m.
____午
zhōng

____午
xià
6:00 p.m.

上 上 上

中 中 中 中

下 下 下

在 在 在 在 在 在

走 走 走 走 走 走 走

8 Read the questions and put a tick (✓) beside the correct answer.

① 現在幾點鐘？ `01:40` p.m.

☐ 上午一點四十分。

☐ 下午一點四十分。

② 還有五分鐘八點，請問現在幾點鐘？

☐ 七點五十五分。

☐ 八點五分。

③ 明天你在不在家？

☐ 我今天下午不在家。

☐ 我明天上午在家。

④ 今天星期二，明天你在家嗎？

☐ 星期三我不在家。

☐ 明天我在不在家。

Typing Records `Go 100`

9 Go to the *Exercise* > *Sentence Quiz* in your Go100 CD and take the quiz (Level 3 or 4). Choose the best two results.

Record	Date	Time Elapsed	Sentence Quiz (Level 3 or 4)	Accurate Spelling per Minute
1				
2				

打電話
Making a Phone Call

1 Read the dialogues and put a tick (✓) beside the correct sentences.

① ☺：請問你找誰？

☻：☐ 我是謝小明。
　　☐ 請問謝小明在家嗎？

② ☺：你家電話是2755767嗎？

☻：☐ 不是，我家電話是2755767。
　　☐ 不是，請問你找誰？

③ ☺：☐ 請問大關在家嗎？
　　☐ 請問你是大關的媽媽嗎？

☻：對不起，他不在家。

④ ☺：☐ 星期六，你哥哥在不在家？
　　☐ 星期六，你在家嗎？

☻：星期六我在家，我等你。

⑤ ☺：請問小明在不在？

☻：☐ 請你等一等，小明不在家。
　　☐ 在，請你等一下。

2 Rearrange the words to form a complete sentence.

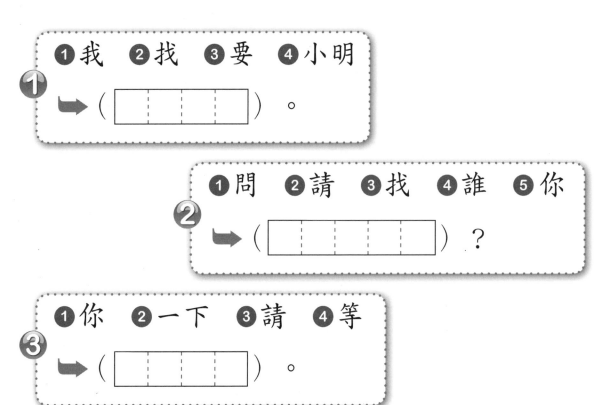

❶我　❷找　❸要　❹小明

➊ ➡ (　│　│　│　) 。

❶問　❷請　❸找　❹誰　❺你

➋ ➡ (　│　│　│　│　) ？

❶你　❷一下　❸請　❹等

➌ ➡ (　│　│　│　) 。

❶他　❷家　❸不在　❹現在

➍ ➡ (　│　│　│　) 。

❶有人　❷找　❸打電話　❹哥哥

➎ ➡ (　│　│　│　) 。

❶我　❷你哥哥　❸找　❹要

➏ ➡ (　│　│　│　) 。

3 Each radical component is represented by a unique number. Form the Chinese characters by combining the components.

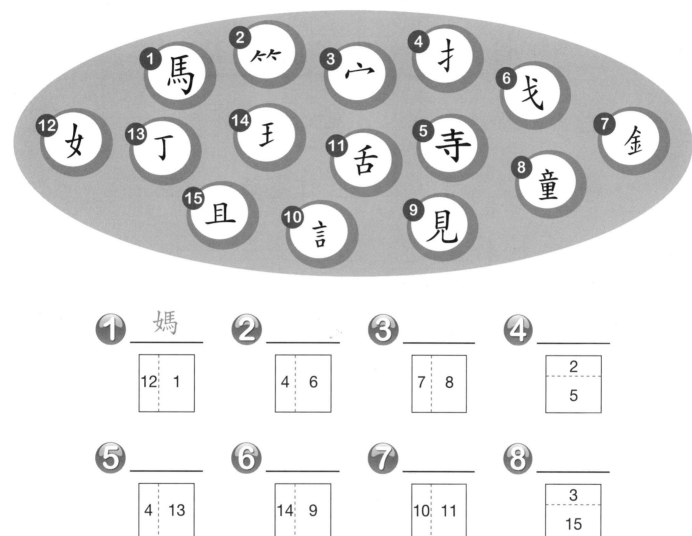

① 竹媽

12	1

②

4	6

③

7	8

④

2
5

⑤

4	13

⑥

14	9

⑦

10	11

⑧

3
15

Typing Records Go100

4 Go to the *Exercise > Sentence Quiz* in your Go100 CD and take the quiz (Level 1 or 2). Choose the best two results.

Record	Date	Time Elapsed	Sentence Quiz (Level 1 or 2)	Accurate Spelling per Minute
1				
2				

5 Practice the strokes to write the characters.

dǎ	huà	lái	shéi	zhǎo
打	話	來	誰	找

☺：姊姊，有人＿＿電＿＿找你。
　　　　　　　　dǎ　　　　huà

☻：我＿＿了，是＿＿打電話＿＿我？
　　　　lái　　　　shéi　　　　zhǎo

打 打 打 打 打
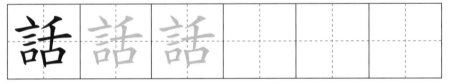

話 話 話 話 話 話 話 話 話 話 話 話

來 來 來 來 來 來 來 來

誰 誰 誰 誰 誰 誰 誰 誰 誰 誰 誰 誰 誰 誰

找 找 找 找 找 找 找

6 Find the words with the Finals "ao" and "ei" , and the Initial "d" in Lesson 9. Then write the *pinyin* of the words in the blanks provided.

ao: _____hào_____ 、 _____

ei: _____ 、 _____

d: _____ 、 _____

7 Fill in the blanks using "那" or "哪".

1 ＿＿＿一位是我爸爸。

2 ☺：他找＿＿＿一位？ ☻：他找小明的姊姊。

3 ＿＿＿一個星期天，你要找小明？

4 ＿＿＿一個電話不好，我不要。

5 這個太貴了，我要買＿＿＿個。

Typing Records Go100

8 Go to the *Exercise > Sentence Quiz* in your Go100 CD and take the quiz (Level 3 or 4). Choose the best two results.

Record	Date	Time Elapsed	Sentence Quiz (Level 3 or 4)	Accurate Spelling per Minute
1				
2				

好老師
A Good Teacher

1 Use the words in the box to complete the sentences. Fill in the blanks with the number that represents the word.

❶ 要	❷ 在	❸ 不在	❹ 會	❺ 不會
❻ 可以	❼ 不可以	❽ 有	❾ 沒有	

① 明天你＿＿＿＿家嗎？

② 他＿＿＿＿一個哥哥。

③ 你＿＿＿＿打人，打人是不對的。
dǎ rén　　dǎ rén

④ 星期一我在學校，我＿＿＿＿家。
xué xiào

⑤ 我＿＿＿＿一點兒中文。

⑥ 二月＿＿＿＿三十日。

⑦ 星期六我＿＿＿＿去你家嗎？

⑧ 我＿＿＿＿的字，可以問老師。

⑨ 請問你＿＿＿＿買什麼？

2 Write the *pinyin* of the following words and translate them into English.

	Chinese	*pinyin*	English
1	老師		
2	同學		
3	一起		
4	可以		
5	有用		
6	不會		
7	學生		
8	等一等		
9	學中文		
10	一點兒		

Typing Records Go 100

3 Go to the *Exercise > Sentence Quiz* in your Go100 CD and take the quiz (Level 1 or 2). Choose the best two results.

Record	Date	Time Elapsed	Sentence Quiz (Level 1 or 2)	Accurate Spelling per Minute
1				
2				

4 **Practice the strokes to write the characters.**

hé	xué	huì	kě	yǐ
和	學	會	可	以

我＿＿＿同學一起＿＿＿中文，
　　　hé　　　　　　　xué

不＿＿＿的字＿＿＿　＿＿＿問老師。
　　huì　　　　　kě　　　yǐ

和和和和和和和和

和	和	和				

學學學學學學學學學學學學學學學學

學	學	學			

會會會會會會會會會會會會會

會	會	會			

可可可可可

可	可	可			

以以以以以

以	以	以			

5 Complete each sentence using the words in the brackets.

1 王老師＿＿＿＿＿＿（教／學）我們中文。

2 我＿＿＿＿＿＿（要／不要）學中文，中文很有用。

3 請問＿＿＿＿＿＿（不在／現在）幾點鐘？

4 請問你找＿＿＿＿＿＿（那一位／哪一位）？

5 我可以＿＿＿＿＿＿（等／等一等）你一起走。

6 你＿＿＿＿＿＿（會／不會）中文，可以問老師。

7 我會＿＿＿＿＿＿（一點半／一點兒）中文，學中文很有用。

Typing Records Go 100

6 Go to the *Exercise* > *Sentence Quiz* in your Go100 CD and take the quiz (Level 3 or 4). Choose the best two results.

Record	Date	Time Elapsed	Sentence Quiz (Level 3 or 4)	Accurate Spelling per Minute
1				
2				

7 Rearrange the words to form a complete sentence.

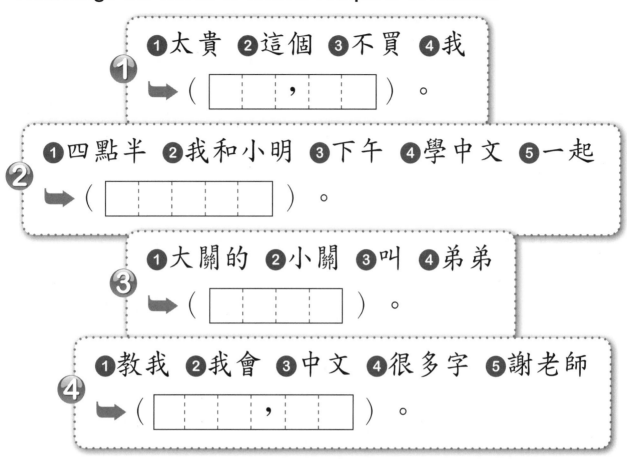

①❶太貴 ❷這個 ❸不買 ❹我
➡ (　｜　，　｜　) 。

②❶四點半 ❷我和小明 ❸下午 ❹學中文 ❺一起
➡ (　｜　｜　｜　) 。

③❶大關的 ❷小關 ❸叫 ❹弟弟
➡ (　｜　｜　) 。

④❶教我 ❷我會 ❸中文 ❹很多字 ❺謝老師
➡ (　｜　，　｜　) 。

8 Using the helping words in the box, translate the following English sentences into Chinese.

老師　教　中文　同學　一起　有用　會

① He is my teacher; he teaches me Chinese.

他是我的老師。他教我中文。

② My classmate and I learn Chinese together.

_____

③ Learning Chinese is very useful. Do you know Chinese?

_____

REVIEW 2

1 Fill in the blanks with the correct Chinese character and *pinyin*.

① 我＿＿＿＿爸爸、＿＿＿＿、一個 姊姊 和一個
      yǒu   mā ma

弟弟 ，我家＿＿＿＿五口人。
          yí gòng

② 大關 現在 不在家，我 等一下 再打電話

＿＿＿＿他。
zhǎo

③ 我 和 同學 一起＿＿＿＿＿＿，不會的字＿＿＿＿
               xué zhōng wén   kě yǐ

問 老師 。

④ 現在＿＿＿＿八點五十分，＿＿＿＿十分鐘九點，九
     shàng wǔ   hái yǒu

點半 時 我要 走 。

2 Look at the schedule below and answer the following questions in Chinese.

Session	Duration	Fee per Person*	
1	10:25 - 11:35	Mon. - Fri.	$8.00
		Sat. - Sun.	$10.00
2	14:30 – 15:40	Mon. - Fri.	$12.00
		Sat. - Sun.	$14.00
3	19:50 – 21:00	Mon. - Fri.	$15.00
		Sat. - Sun.	$17.00

* Kids (under 12) & Senior citizens (above 65): Half Price

1 星期六下午，小宜（十歲）和哥哥（十五歲）一起
看表演 (watch the performance) ，他們一共要付(pay)多少錢？
<small>kàn biǎo yǎn   fù</small>

_____

2 星期五晚上，王老師和他爸爸（六十三歲）一起看
表演，他們一共要付多少錢？

_____

3 Look at the composition of the characters and identify the odd one out.

1 (2) **❶** 話   **❷** 星   **❸** 錢   **❹** 誰

2 (   ) **❶** 半   **❷** 弟   **❸** 中   **❹** 教

3 (   ) **❶** 學   **❷** 家   **❸** 明   **❹** 星

4 (   ) **❶** 位   **❷** 晚   **❸** 五   **❹** 妹

5 (   ) **❶** 媽   **❷** 姊   **❸** 哥   **❹** 你

4 Fill in the blanks to complete the conversation.

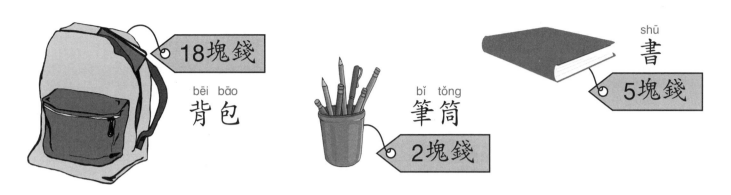

18塊錢
bēi bāo
背包

bǐ tǒng
筆筒
2塊錢

shū
書
5塊錢

☺：請問一個筆筒多少錢，兩個背包多少錢？

☻：一個筆筒＿＿＿塊錢，兩個背包＿＿＿塊錢。

☺：我有10塊錢，＿＿＿＿＿太貴了，我不買。

　　　＿＿＿＿＿很便宜，我可以買五個。

5 Each of the following sentences contains an extra character. Circle it.

① 明天大關在不在家⑭？

② 對，我是大關的姊姊嗎。

③ 那一位是不是小明的爸爸。

④ 現在是下午三點五分鐘。

⑤ 我沒有一個哥哥，還有一個弟弟。

6 Answer the questions according to the information provided.

	Sun.	Mon.	Tue.	Wed.	Thu.	Fri.	Sat.
小明	*swim in the afternoon	3:30p.m. to 5:30p.m. join a band	9:00a.m. to 12:00p.m. learn Chinese	9:00a.m. to 12:00p.m. learn Chinese	8:40a.m. to 9:30a.m. *play piano	3:30p.m. to 6:30p.m. learn Chinese	1:30p.m. to 6:00p.m. visit my classmate

	Sun.	Mon.	Tue.	Wed.	Thu.	Fri.	Sat.
大關	swim in the afternoon	-	9:00a.m. to 12:00p.m. learn Chinese	3:30p.m. to 6:30p.m. learn Chinese	8:40p.m. to 9:30p.m. play piano	3:30p.m. to 6:30p.m. learn Chinese	1:30p.m. to 6:00p.m. visit my classmate

	Sun.	Mon.	Tue.	Wed.	Thu.	Fri.	Sat.
家家	swim in the afternoon	3:30p.m. to 5:30p.m. join a band	9:00a.m. to 12:00p.m. learn Chinese	3:30p.m. to 6:30p.m. learn Chinese	8:40p.m. to 9:30p.m. play piano	3:30p.m. to 6:30p.m. learn Chinese	1:30p.m. to 1:36p.m. call my classmate

* swim 游泳　* play piano 彈鋼琴

1 我星期二、星期三和星期五學中文。

我星期日上午不用上學。

我星期六下午不在家。

　　　　　　　　　　　　　　　　　　　tán gāng qín
我星期四晚上八點四十分到九點三十分彈鋼琴。

我是 ＿＿＿＿＿＿ 。

2 我星期三上午不用學中文。

　　　　　　　　　yóu yǒng
我星期日和同學一起游泳。

我星期六下午打電話找同學。

我星期四晚上八點四十分到九點半彈鋼琴。

我是 ＿＿＿＿＿＿ 。

7 Read the passage below and answer the questions.

大關今年十歲，他有兩個哥哥，一個姊姊和兩個弟弟。他家一共八口人。大關星期一到星期五和哥哥一起學中文。大關的中文老師叫謝宜。大關會一點兒中文，還會打中文字*。明年大關還要學中文，他說學中文很有用。

* 打中文字 type Chinese character

① 大關今年幾歲？

_____

② 大關有幾個姊姊？

_____

③ 大關家一共有幾口人？

_____

④ 大關的哥哥會中文嗎？

_____

⑤ 大關的中文老師姓什麼？

_____

⑥ 大關明年還要學中文嗎？

_____

8. Look at the three groups of phrases below. Form complete sentences by selecting one or two phrases from each group.

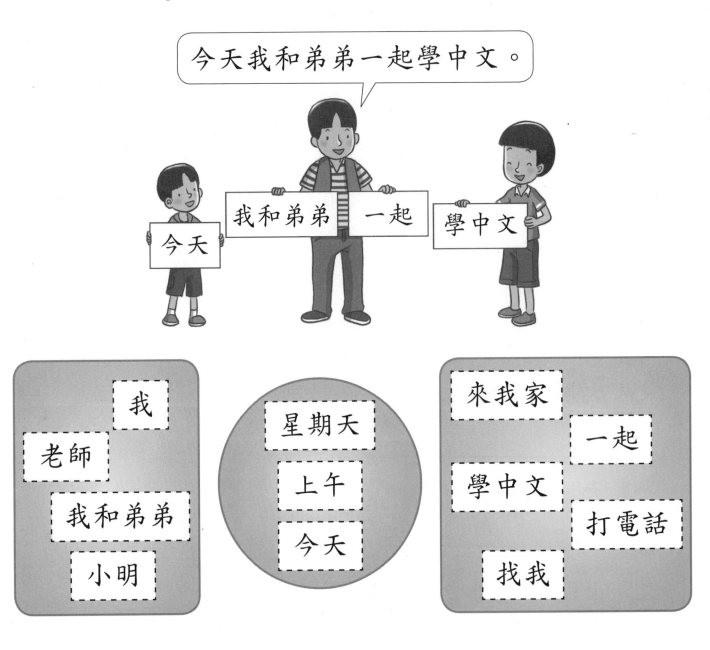

今天我和弟弟一起學中文。

今天　我和弟弟　一起　學中文

我
老師
我和弟弟
小明

星期天
上午
今天

來我家
一起
學中文
打電話
找我

1 _____

2 _____

3 _____